First published in the UK in 2018 by i-Read Ltd,
Unit 7, Hatfield Regis Grange Farm, Hatfield Broad Oak,
Bishops Stortford, Hertfordshire CM22 7JZ

www.i-read.co.uk

ISBN: 978-1-78550-200-2

Illustrated by Christine Jenny

Printed in Malaysia

North Pole

Fairy Fee

Baby's first Christmas

Lion as Santa

Frosty the Snowman

Frog loves Santa

Santa's Donkey

Christmas Owl

Ginger House Baker

Sheep Elf

Santa on his way

Christmas Cake

Christmas is so
much fun!

Santa's Dasher

Goat Rudolph